Gulliver's Travels

Jonathan Swift

Simplified by D K Swan
and Michael West

Illustrated by Victor Ambrus

Longman Group UK Limited,
Longman House, Burnt Mill, Harlow,
Essex CM20 2JE, England
and Associated Companies throughout the world.

First published 1987
Seventh impression 1992

ISBN 0-582-52285-4

Set in 12/14 point Linotron 202 Versailles
Produced by Longman Group (FE) Limited
Printed in Hong Kong

Acknowledgements

The cover background is a wallpaper design called NUAGE, courtesy of Osborne and Little plc.

Stage 2: 900 word vocabulary

Please look under *New words* at the back of this book for explanations of words outside this stage.

Contents

Introduction

Jonathan Swift

Swift was an Irishman, born in Dublin in 1667, but of an old English family. After completing his university education at Trinity College, Dublin, he began work in England as secretary to the important writer and statesman Sir William Temple.

Jonathan Swift soon became an important figure among the writers and politicians of London. He had ideas about writing and about political matters – public affairs and government – which he could put into words very clearly and cleverly. His political friends were glad to have him on their side. His political enemies feared him.

In 1714, Queen Anne died, and those political enemies came to power. Swift went back to Ireland, where he was already the Dean of St Patrick's Cathedral in Dublin. At first, he had few friends there. But between 1720 and 1730 he wrote very strongly on the side of the Irish. They felt that their rulers, the English, treated them unfairly – even cruelly at times. And it was good to have a writer like Swift to attack the unfairness for them. He had a command of language that made his attacks and his satire bite deeply. That writing brought him a great many friends in Dublin and in other parts of Ireland.

It was during this time that Swift wrote *Gulliver's Travels,* which appeared in the bookshops in 1726.

Gulliver's Travels

At the beginning of the eighteenth century, books about travel to unknown places were of great interest to the reading public in Britain. Readers had enjoyed true accounts like William Dampier's *New Voyage* (1697), which described his visits to the coasts of what are now called Australia and New Zealand.

Then came Daniel Defoe's *Robinson Crusoe* (1719). Defoe did not pretend that his story of Crusoe's life on an island was true. But he wrote in the style of the true accounts. Like the true accounts, *Robinson Crusoe* dealt with happenings and things seen, not with thoughts or feelings.

Swift saw the importance of that style. He didn't want to make his readers believe that the impossible lands in *Gulliver's Travels* were true or real. But he did want to make them think.

Gulliver's Travels is satire. Readers find themselves looking at their own world, its beliefs and customs, with new eyes. Lemuel Gulliver describes the different places and their inhabitants in a simple style. He gives us facts and figures, not opinions, about them. And so we don't just laugh at them: we put ourselves in the place of the Lilliputians and others, and we see ourselves as they would see us. We laugh at ourselves, and – Swift hoped – decide to change some of our more foolish or unpleasant ways.

Because the style is so simple, and because Swift makes us enjoy his story, *Gulliver's Travels* (usually in a shortened form) has been a favourite children's book for a long time. But it would be a mistake to see it as just a children's story; Swift wanted his readers to think seriously about the world they live in.

A journey to Lilliput

Chapter 1
How I came to Lilliput

My father had some land in the north of England, but it was not very much, and I was the youngest of five brothers. I left school when I was seventeen years old, because my father could not pay for me after that. I then went on to the ship *Antelope,* which was sailing under Captain Pritchard for the South Seas. We set out from Bristol in May, 1700 , and at first we had an easy time.

I will not write down everything that happened to us in those seas. It is enough to say that, on our way to the East Indies, a great wind carried us the wrong way so that we came to the north of Van Diemen's Land. Twelve of our men had died from the hard work and bad food, and of the rest none was very strong. One morning, when there was heavy rain so that we could not see well, one of the men saw a rock very close to the ship. The wind was so strong that we were driven on it, and a great hole was made in the bottom of the ship. Six of us got a boat into the sea. But we were not strong enough, and the wind soon turned it over.

I do not know what happened to the others, but I believe that they must all have been lost. I myself was carried by the wind and water. I do not know which way I went – or how far.

At last I was sure that I was going to die. But I put my feet down, and found that I could stand. By this time the wind was much less. I walked more than a kilometre before I got to dry land. It was after seven at night then. I went on about half a kilometre, but I could not see any houses or people – or perhaps I was so tired that I did not see them. Then I lay down on the grass, which was very short and soft, and fell into the deepest sleep that I ever had in my life.

I must have slept for about nine hours. When I awoke it was just daylight. I was lying on my back. I tried to get up from the ground, but I could not move! Then I found that my arms and feet were held down to the ground with strings. My hair, which was long, was held down in the same way. Thousands of strings had been passed across my body, so that I could not move. I could only lie there on my back looking up at the sky.

The sun grew hot, and the light hurt my eyes. I heard noise all around me, but I could see

Gulliver's ship

nothing. In a little time I felt something alive moving on my foot. Then it came over my body and up to my face. Turning my eyes down as much as I could, I saw a man. He was less than fifteen centimetres high. By his dress he seemed to be a soldier. Then forty more little men like him followed.

I was so much surprised that I gave a great cry. They all ran back in great fear, and (as I was told later) some of them were hurt in jumping down from my side on to the ground. They soon came back, and one, braver than the rest, came so far that he could see my face. He threw up his hands and raised his eyes and cried out in a very clear voice, *"Hekinah degul."* And the others answered, *"Hekinah? Degul hekinah!"* But I did not then know what they meant.

After pulling very hard I got one arm up from the ground. I also raised my head; this gave me great pain, for many of the hairs were pulled out. I put out my hand to catch some of the little men, but they ran away before I could catch them. Then I heard a noise, and felt a pricking in my hand like that of a thousand needles, and I found that they were shooting at me. Many of the little arrows went into my clothes and did not hurt me, but others were shot up into the air and came down on my face. They caused me great pain, and I was afraid for my eyes. I put my hand over my face.

After this I thought that the wisest thing to do was to lie quiet till night. I thought that then I could quickly set free the rest of my body. I thought that I had no cause to be afraid of the people, if they were no larger than those that I had seen.

But things did not happen in this way. When the people saw that I was quiet, they did not shoot at me any more, but by the noise I knew that their numbers had become greater.

Soon I heard a sound, near my ear. Turning my head a little I saw that some men were building a wooden table, large enough for four of the little people to stand upon, and about forty-five centimetres high. When the table was ready, four of the little people got up on it. One of them was older and rather larger than the other three. He had a beautiful coat which was held up from the ground by a little boy who stood behind him. He called out, *"Langro dehul san."*

At once forty of the people came and cut the strings which held the other side of my head, so that I could turn it and see the people on the table better. Then the man with the long coat began to speak. He spoke very well, moving his hands this way and that so as to show his meaning. He spoke for a long time. Of course, I did not know the words, but from his hands and from his voice I thought that he was telling me that they would not hurt me if I did as I was ordered, but that they

The little people hold Gulliver down with string

would kill me if I tried to get free. I raised my hand and turned up my eyes to the sky to show that I knew what he meant and that I would remain quiet. I also put my hand to my mouth, showing that I wanted food. I had had nothing to eat for some hours before I left the ship.

He seemed to know what I wanted. He gave some orders, and at once a hundred men climbed up on to my body and marched up to my mouth, carrying food. These things had been sent there by the king when he first heard about me. I did not know what the food was. There were things not larger than mice; I thought perhaps they were cows cooked whole. There were also hens no bigger than a bean. I ate the loaves of bread two or three at a time. As I ate there were cries of surprise from the people because I could eat so quickly and so much.

After I had eaten I showed them that I wanted to drink. Then a great many men came carrying a great pot of milk which they poured into my mouth. I called for another, and they gave it to me. But, when I called for a third, they showed me that they had no more. I had drunk all the milk in the country. So pleased were they at the sight of my eating and drinking that they danced upon my body and my arms crying out, *"Hekinah degul!"*

After I had eaten, there came to me a very great

person bringing a letter from the king. He was followed by many servants dressed in very fine clothes. He walked up to my face and held out his letter close to my eyes. Then he spoke for some time, and several times pointed to the north-west. As I learnt later, he was pointing to their city, which was about a kilometre away. He seemed to be saying that the king had ordered that I must be carried to the city.

I answered in a few words, and I showed with my hand that I wanted to be set free. He knew what I meant, but he moved his head as if saying, "No, you must be carried." But he showed me that they would give me food and drink and that no one would hurt me. Seeing the great number of them, and remembering the pain of the shooting, I said that they might do what they wished. The great man then went away, very pleased with himself.

Soon after that I heard a great noise of the people, and there were cries of, "*Peplom selan.*" Then a lot of people came on one side of me and cut all the strings on that side so that I could now turn on to the other side. I was glad to do that. They also put on my face some oil which had a nice smell and took away all the pain of the shots. This, and the food that I had eaten, made me sleepy. I slept for about nine hours. (I learnt later that they had mixed a sleeping-powder with my food.)

As soon as the king had heard of my coming, he had ordered his men to bring me to the city. He had told them to make a great cart to carry me.

They brought the great cart just behind my back, then they had to raise me and put me on it. Nine hundred men worked for three hours, and at last they got me into place on the cart. They did it while I was lying in a deep sleep because of the powder. Fifteen hundred of the king's largest horses were to pull me to the city.

After four hours we began our journey. We made a long march, then we rested at night with five hundred men on each side of me ready to shoot me if I tried to move. Next day, at daylight, we went on, and at noon we were about a hundred and fifty metres from the city. The king came out to meet me; he came near and looked at me, but his wise men did not think it was safe for him to climb up on me.

At the place where the cart stopped there was an old church. It was the largest building in the whole country. It had now been made ready for me to use as my house. The great door on the north was more than a metre high and nearly a metre wide. So I could go into it by getting down on my hands. One of my feet was set in a great ring on the end of many strong strings so that I could not get away, but could only walk about a metre away from the outside of my door.

Chapter 2
How I lived in Lilliput

Early next day I came out of my house and looked around me. The country was like a garden. The fields were about twelve metres square. The tallest trees seemed to be about two metres high. On the other side of me the city looked like a picture in a child's book. In front of my church there was a very big house on the other side of the road, about six metres away from me. As I stood there, the king came with a great many ladies and gentlemen. They went up on to the top of the house to look at me. After a time the king came down. He got up on his horse and began to ride nearer to me. But the horse was afraid of such a sight, as if a mountain had moved in front of him. The king (who was a very good horseman) was not thrown off, but, when servants came and held the horse for him, he got down. Then he began to walk round me, but he did not come near, into the part I could reach.

Food was then brought to me on carts. The queen and the young princes sat on the top of the house and watched me eating.

After a time the king went away. A number of soldiers stayed to keep the people from coming too close to me, or hurting me. But, when I was sitting on the ground near the door of my house, some of the people shot at me; one of the shots nearly hit my eye. Then the captain ordered his soldiers to catch six of the men who had done this. He made the soldiers throw them to me so that I could punish them. I held five of them in one hand, and I took the other and raised him to my mouth, as if I wanted to eat him. He cried out in fear, and the captain and his soldiers were very unhappy at the sight. But I laughed and put the six men carefully on the ground, and let them run away. The people and the soldiers seemed to be very pleased at my gentleness, and they told the king about it.

The king and all his great men had met together to talk about me. Some were afraid that I might get free – which might be very dangerous. Others were afraid that my food would cost them a great deal of money, and that the people of the country would not have enough to eat. Some thought that perhaps it might be best to kill me (they could do it in my sleep). But others thought that if they did that, the smell of the dead body might cause illness in the city. While they were saying these things, the captain of the soldiers came and told them how I had treated the six men. The great men were very pleased and said that they should keep me alive. The king ordered six very wise men to teach me, so that I could speak to them and know what they said.

All this was done, and in about three weeks I

The city was like a picture in a child's book

could speak quite well. The king often came to see me and helped my teachers. We began to talk to each other. One of the first things that I said to him was that I wished to be set free. He answered that this could not be done at once, but he must think about it.

Then he said, "I hope you will not be angry if I tell some of my soldiers to look at the things you carry about with you. I am afraid that you may have some things which might be dangerous to me and to my people."

I answered, "I shall be glad to show your men everything that I have."

The next day two men came and walked all over me looking into all parts of my clothing. They drew pictures of all my things and made notes on each thing – my pencil, my notebook, my pipe, the glasses which I used for my weak eyesight, and all the other things that I had with me.

At last the king sent me certain "Orders", saying that, if I would keep to these, he would let me go free.

Orders of
Golbasto Momaren Evlame Gurdilo
Shefin mully Ully Gue,
King of Lilliput, Giant among Men,
Loved and Feared by all peoples
upon Earth.

1 The Man-Mountain shall not leave our country without our orders.

2 He shall not come into the city without our orders. (Two hours before he comes into the city all the people shall go into their houses and remain there.)

3 He shall walk only upon the roads. He shall not walk over the fields, or lie down in them.

4 When he walks, he shall take great care not to put his foot upon any of our people, or on their horses, or on their carts; and he shall not take them up in his hands.

5 He shall help our ships and our army in the war against the people of the Island of Blefusco.

6 He shall help our workmen to raise certain great stones for building a wall round our garden.

7 He shall be given such food as would be enough for 1728 of our people.

The reader will notice the number 1728. It was found by the king's learned men that I was twelve times as high as any one of the people of Lilliput. My mass would then be 12 × 12 × 12 times that of a man of Lilliput. 12 times 12 is 144; 144 × 12 is 1728.

Chapter 3
How I made war on Blefusco

Reldresal, a great man in Lilliput, and a close friend of the king, came and talked to me. He told me that there had been quarrels in Lilliput for many years. "There are two sides to the quarrel," he said, "the Big-enders and the Little-enders. The king himself is a Little-ender, and so are most of our people, but the Big-enders are helped by the people of the Island of Blefusco. War has already started. With quarrels inside the country and war outside I am greatly afraid. I do not know what will happen. Perhaps you can help us. If you cannot, we are lost."

"But," said I, "what is this quarrel about? And what is a 'Big-ender'?"

"The quarrel," answered Reldresal, "is about a very solemn matter. It is about a thing which comes into the lives of all our people almost every day. It is about the way in which an egg should be opened for eating. The Big-enders believe that the big end of the egg should be cut off, and the Little-enders believe that it is the little end which should be cut."

I went to the king next day and told him that I could help him in the war if he would let me do so. "I have heard," I said, "that the ships of Blefusco are waiting to come against you as soon as they can get the right wind. They know nothing about me, because I have not been near the sea since I first came here." I told him what I would do, and he was very pleased.

I then went to the captains of some of our ships and asked them how deep the water was between the Island of Lilliput and the Island of Blefusco. I learnt that it was not more than a metre and a half, or two metres at the deepest part. So I got a long piece of the strongest string that I could find. Then I took off my shoes and walked into the water.

In half an hour I came to Blefusco and saw their ships. When they saw me many of the men jumped out of their ships into the water. I took my string and passed it round the front part of each of the ships, so that they were all held together. While I was doing this they began to shoot at me, and many of the arrows hit my hands and my face. These gave me great pain, but my greatest fear was for my eyes. I had remembered to bring my eye-glasses with me, and I put them on, and after that I felt safe, and could go on with my work. I got all the ships together on my string. I then took the other end of the string, and so pulled forty of the largest of the Blefusco ships after me.

The people on the land sent up a very angry cry, but they could not do anything. When I had got out of danger, I stopped to put some of that sweet-smelling oil on my hands where the arrows had hit them. I also took off my eye-glasses. Then I went on and came to Lilliput.

The king and all his great men had come down to meet me. The first thing they saw was all the Blefusco ships coming, and they were greatly afraid. They could not see me, because the sea was deep there, and only my head was above water. As I came nearer I stood up out of the water, and held up the string so that they could see it, and I called out: "Long live the most powerful King of Lilliput!"

The king was so pleased at this, that he asked me to go again and bring all the rest of the ships from Blefusco. He wanted to conquer their whole country and to make the people of it his servants. He would then be strong enough to put the Big-enders to death and to make himself king of the whole world.

"I won't help you to treat a free people in that way," I said.

He was very angry. And from that time certain of the king's friends began to talk together about how they might kill me or send me away.

About three weeks later, great men from Blefusco came to Lilliput to ask for peace. The King of Lilliput listened to them. There were six great men from Blefusco, and they were so great that about five hundred other men came with them as helpers and writers and servants. Each of the great men spoke for several hours, and then the great men of Lilliput answered – with the help of about six hundred less great men. In the end, the six great men from Blefusco and six great men of Lilliput put their names to the paper that gave peace to the two countries. Of course Lilliput won a great deal of land and ships and other things, and Blefusco lost them. But there was peace, and the paper said that the King of Lilliput and the King of Blefusco were now friends.

The people of Blefusco lost less than they would have lost, because I told the great men of Lilliput to be wise and not to take too much. So the King of Blefusco sent a letter to me, thanking me and asking me to visit his country.

Now, as you remember, it was written in the Orders of the King of Lilliput that I should not leave the country without the king's word, but I did not think that he would say, "No." So I got ready to visit the King of Blefusco. I didn't know that the King of Lilliput was angry and that many of his friends were talking together against me.

That night, one of the king's wise men came to me. He had been my friend, and he told me that I was in danger. The king had heard that I wanted to visit Blefusco. He and his friends were sure that I would make war on Lilliput from there. The king had now given orders to his men to put my eyes out, and to give me no food, so that I would die. There were also orders for taking away my body when I was dead; it was to be cut up and pulled away, piece by piece, and thrown into the sea.

Hearing this, I was at first very angry, and began to think what I could do against these people. But later I thought of all the kindness that they had shown me. "They are only foolish," I said.

Then I took one of the king's largest ships. I took off my clothes. I put my clothes and all the other things that I had into it, so as to keep them dry. Then I walked through the water pulling the ship after me, and came to the Island of Blefusco.

I found two men near the sea who showed me the way to the city. The King of Blefusco and his queen came out to meet me.

I will not tell you of all the kindness shown to me by this great king. He did all that he could to make me happy. But there was no house large enough for me, and I had to put my coat over me and sleep out in a field.

Chapter 4
How I came home again

Three days later I was walking on the north-east of the island and I saw something that looked like a boat a long way out to sea. I took off my shoes and walked out to it. I soon came near to it; it was being brought in to the land by the wind and water. I saw that it was a boat, upside down in the water.

I went quickly back to the city and asked the king to send twenty of his largest ships and two thousand men to help me to get the boat to land. The king's ships sailed round. They put strings on to the boat and drew it in nearer the land where there was less water. Then I took it myself and turned it up the right way, and found that it was quite unbroken and ready for sailing.

I brought it round to the city. The people were very surprised at seeing such a large boat, which was to them as big as a great mountain. I asked the king to give me food and other things that I needed, so that I could go back to my own country. He was sad because I wanted to leave him so soon, but he was very kind and gave me all that I asked. His men also helped me in making the boat ready for sea.

After a few days everything was ready. I took with me six cows, alive, to show them in my own country. I would gladly have taken some of the people, but none of them wanted to come. I think they were afraid.

I set out on 1st May, 1702. The king and queen waved their hands to me as I sailed away. I hoped to reach some of the islands north-east of Van Diemen's Land. But on the third day I saw a ship. I called out to her, but I got no answer. Then the ship came nearer and her men saw me. They put out a flag.

My heart was full of happiness when I saw her English flag. I went on to the ship, taking with me all my things. (I kept the six cows in my hat.) The captain was a very good man. I met among his men an old friend, Peter Williams, who told the captain who I was. After that, the captain was most kind to me. He asked me where I had come from, and I told him some of the things that are written in this book. Of course he did not believe me: he thought that the dangers through which I had passed had made me mad. Then I took out the six cows and showed them to him. He was very surprised, and he believed my story.

I will not tell the reader about the rest of the journey, which was very quiet for most of the way. One of my cows was eaten by the rats on the ship. The rest were alive when I came to England, and I sold some of them for a lot of money.

Gulliver in Brobdingnag

Chapter 1
How I came to Brobdingnag

I was rich after my journey to Lilliput, and I bought a house in England. "I'll live here quietly and be happy," I thought. But I couldn't stay there. I went to sea again.

We sailed towards the Indies to buy and sell things there, but before we could reach the Molucca Islands, a great wind caught us. It blew for day after day and carried our ship far to the east. Our captain did not know where we were.

We had enough food on the ship, but after being driven by the wind for weeks, we needed fresh water.

The wind died, and a few days later we heard the cry, "Land!" It was an unknown country.

The captain sent some men in one of the ship's boats to get fresh water. I went with them.

There was no river near the place where we landed. So we began to look for fresh water by wandering one way and another. I myself went south towards some hills, but I saw no water, and after a time I went back towards the boat.

The boat was not on the sand. It was a long way out to sea. All the other men were in the boat, and they were taking it towards the ship as fast as they could. I was going to shout to them, when I saw the cause of their fear.

A huge creature was walking after them in the sea. The water came only to his knees, but there were so many pointed rocks under it that he could not catch the boat.

I turned and ran away towards the hills that I had seen before.

After a time, I found a very wide road, and I walked along it. On each side there seemed to be a thick forest. I looked up at the forest "trees", but I saw that they were not trees. I was in a field of corn, and the corn was twelve metres high. I was not on a road but on a narrow way for huge men walking across the field.

I heard a great and frightening noise, and suddenly I knew that huge creatures were cutting down the corn all round me. Then I saw one of them. He was walking towards me, and I was afraid that his big foot was going to come down on top of me. I gave a great cry.

The creature heard me and stopped. He looked at the ground all round him, and then he saw me. For a minute he looked at me carefully, the way we look at a small creature to see whether it will bite. Then he took me up in his fingers and held me about three metres away from his eyes. I was about twenty metres from the ground, so I was afraid: I thought that he would throw me down and put his foot on me, as we do with little creatures that we do not like. I put my hands together and asked him not to kill me. That seemed to please him, so I tried to show him that his fingers were hurting my sides.

He understood, and turned up the edge of his coat to make a place for me to lie. Then he took me to the farmer, and put me on the ground.

I took off my hat and spoke to the farmer. He put his hand on the ground and showed me that I should lie on it. Then he held me very close to his ear – about two metres away – but it was clear that he could not understand me. He spoke to me, and the noise was like great guns. I knew that he was speaking words, but they meant nothing to me.

The farmer carried me carefully to his house.

It was about twelve noon, and a servant brought in dinner. The farmer's wife broke some bread and meat into very small pieces and gave them to me on a wooden dish about the height of an English table. I showed my thanks, took out my knife, and began to eat hungrily. That pleased the people round the table – the farmer and his wife, three children, and the farmer's old mother.

I was very tired, and the farmer's wife saw

The huge creature sees Gulliver in the corn

that. She took me to her room, put me on her bed, and went out, locking the door. I slept for about two hours – in all my clothes, and with my sword at my side. When I woke, I looked round me.

The room seemed huge – about a hundred metres wide and sixty metres high – and I was on a bed that was nearly twenty metres wide and about eight metres from the floor.

I was looking at these things when two rats climbed up on to the bed and ran about looking for the cause of the smell that they had noticed. Suddenly one of them came near to me, and I drew out my sword in fright. The two animals were not afraid. One of them tried to bite my arm, and I struck with my sword at its stomach. I made a deep cut, and the rat fell dead. I could not kill the other, but it ran away with a wound in its back.

The creatures were as big as myself, and they moved very quickly. I was glad to be alive.

The farmer had a daughter, nine years old. She was about twelve metres high, but in other ways she was like an English girl of the same age.

She had a doll made of wood, with doll's clothes and a doll's house to play with. She and her mother made the doll's bed into a bed for me. Their finest cloth was like the stuff our ships' sails are made of, but I liked my bed, and I was safe in the doll's house from rats and other animals.

The farmer's daughter was also my teacher. When I pointed to something, she told me its name or the word for it. So in a few days I was able to ask for anything I wanted. It was she who first called me *Grildrig*. Her family used that name, and later, when the whole country heard about me, everybody knew me as *Grildrig*. It means a very small man.

She looked after me every minute of every day and night while I was in that country, which they called *Brobdingnag*. I am alive today because she saved me again and again. I called her my *glumdalclitch*, my little keeper, and I am sad because in the end I must have made her very unhappy.

People in the villages near the farm heard that the farmer had found a very small creature in the fields.

"This creature," they told each other, "is only as big as a *splacknuck*, but in other ways like a very small man. It seems to speak words of its own, and it has already learnt some of our words. It stands and walks on two legs like us, although its legs are very small and weak. It wears clothes, and it has a very small sword." (A *splacknuck* was an animal, less than two metres long.)

The head man of a village which was not far away came to see me. He was most surprised when the farmer put me on the table and I spoke to him.

This visitor spoke to the farmer for a long

time. I saw that they were talking about me, and I also saw that their talk was making Glumdalclitch more and more unhappy.

When the visitor went away, the little girl told me why she was unhappy. She was weeping as she told me about their plan to show me on the next market day in the nearest town. She was afraid that some of the country people would take me in their hands and hurt me. But she was more afraid that being shown for money like that would hurt my feelings.

The farmer took no notice of Glumdalclitch when she prayed him not to show me. The next market day he took me to the nearest town. He had made a box for me, with a door for me to go in and out, and a few holes to let in air. He carried me in this on his horse, and his daughter sat behind him. She had put the softest bed-cover from her doll's house into the box for me to lie down on, but I had a very bad journey. The horse went about twelve metres at every step, and it moved so far up and down that my ride was like being in a ship when a great wind is blowing.

The journey only lasted about half an hour because the town was only forty kilometres away, but I was already tired when we reached it. Then the farmer took a room near the market and showed me on a table to about thirty people at one time.

Glumdalclitch stood on a chair beside the

table to take care of me and to give me orders and ask questions. The questions were those that she had taught me to answer.

"What is your name?" she asked in the language of Brobdingnag.

"My name," I said in the same language, "is Lemuel Gulliver." I had to shout to make them hear me.

"Where do you come from?"

"I come from England."

"Why are you so small?"

"I am not small. I am as big as the other men in England. You and your people are huge; you are giants."

The people laughed then, and the great noise hurt my ears and made me feel weak.

Then I had to walk about on the table and take my hat off to the people. I drank to wish them good health, using a doll's cup. I drew my sword and showed them the way we use it in fighting. And I did other things they wanted to see me do.

The farmer showed me like that twelve times that day. After that, and after a very bad journey back to the farm, I was very tired and ill.

But there was no rest for me. The farmer wanted more and more money, and he showed me not only on market days but every day at his farm, because people came from many parts of the country to see me. Glumdalclitch was very unhappy as she saw me getting weaker and weaker. But the farmer took no notice of her.

Chapter 2
How I met the king and queen

The farmer thought that I was going to die because I was so ill. Instead of showing me less, he wanted to make as much money as he could before my death. He began to show me in the big cities, beginning with Lorbrulgrud, the greatest city in Brobdingnag, where the king had his palace.

Not long after we arrived there, a palace servant came and ordered the farmer to bring me at once to the palace to show me to the queen.

I hoped that the queen would save me, and so I fell on my knees on the table in front of her. She very kindly put out her little finger towards me, and I put both my arms round it and kissed the end of it.

The queen asked me some questions about my country and my travels, and I answered as clearly and in as few words as I could.

"Would you like to live in the palace?" she asked me in her own language.

"I think I am the farmer's servant," I answered, "but if the farmer will set me free, I will gladly serve here in the palace."

The farmer was asked to sell me, and he was happy to take a thousand pieces of gold (each as big as the biggest English wheel).

I asked the queen to take the farmer's daughter as her servant. I said, "She has looked after me with great care and understanding, and I would like her to go on looking after me."

The queen was glad to do that, and the farmer did not mind leaving her. Glumdalclitch herself was very happy. So the farmer went away alone.

The queen then took me to the king.

The king was working – reading and putting his name to huge pieces of paper. He looked up when the queen came in. He saw me on her hand but he did not look closely at me.

"Since when," he asked the queen, "have you liked *splacknucks*?"

The queen laughed. She put me on my feet on the king's desk and ordered me to tell him about myself. I told him in a few words.

He asked me some questions, and I answered him. At first he thought I might be a very well made doll or plaything, with clockwork inside me. But he saw that that could not be true, so he sent for the three wisest men in the country.

The three did not listen to me or ask questions. They looked at me, watched me, talked about me for hours. Then they spoke to the king.

"This thing," they said, "isn't an animal. It can't fly, or run very fast, or climb trees, or make holes in the ground, and so it can't save its own life. We are sure that it isn't a very small person because the smallest grown-up person in the world is more than five times as high. We know it isn't a doll because it's too weak to have been made by men's hands. So we must tell you that it is certainly a Thing – a thing that was not planned – a Mistake."

I spoke to the king myself. "I am *not* a Thing," I said. "I come from a country where there are several million men and women, all of my height. The animals, trees, and houses are all the right height for people like me. We have our own language and our own king, our own laws, and our own way of life."

I told him a great many things about England and the other countries of Europe. He listened carefully. The he sent the wise men away.

"I must hear more from this creature," he told the queen. "Make a safe place for the little creature to live in."

The queen sent for the best woodworker in the land and told him to make a box for me, following my own plans. He was a very good worker, and in three weeks I had a wooden room, about five metres long, five metres wide, and three metres high. It had two windows and a door, and the top could be taken off to let Glumdalclitch clean the room and take my bed out in the morning and put it in at night. It had metal to make the bottom strong, and there was a ring in the top to carry it by.

The queen liked me so much that at dinner time I

always sat at my own table on her dinner table. She cut me the smallest pieces of food and watched me while I cut them up with my own knife and ate them.

Every Wednesday (which was their day of rest like our Sunday) the king and all his family had dinner together. Then the king liked to have me at my table near him. He asked me questions about Europe and its people, its laws and learning, the things its people believed, and the way they were ruled.

Sometimes, when I spoke too proudly about my own country, England – about our wars, the riches of our great families, the quarrels between our churchmen, our rulers and Parliament – the king laughed, making a great noise. Once he said to the queen: "This shows us the foolishness of being proud. We think we are great, but we find that even funny little creatures like this one think that they are great too. Perhaps they too have proud rulers and landowners, rich lords and beautiful ladies. Perhaps they make little living places and holes near to each other and call them great cities. Perhaps they try to dress in finer clothes than the other little creatures, and love each other, and quarrel, and fight, and say bad things about one friend to another friend – just like us – just like real people."

Of course I was angry. He was talking about England – England the Home of the Great, the Winner of Wars, the Jewel of Europe, Leader of

The queen gives small pieces of food to Gulliver

the World in Goodness and Truth... But I couldn't *do* anything. And I began to ask myself whether I was right to be angry. After I had been in the country for several months, seeing only them and their things, and never hearing the voices of smaller people, I stopped thinking that they were huge and ugly and noisy.

If I had then seen a company of English lords and ladies dressed in their finest clothes, and behaving as they do in the city or in the king's palace, I should have wanted to laugh at them as much as the King of Brobdingnag and his people laughed at me.

The king was a ruler of great understanding. He often ordered his people to bring me to him.

He wanted to hear me speak about my own country, and I was glad to do so.

"Our land," I told him, "is made up of three great countries under one powerful ruler. The three countries are contained in two islands, but the ruler also rules a great deal of land in America."

He asked me how big the islands were, and then he asked very many questions about the much bigger English lands in America. He could not easily understand why they were not owned by the people who were there before the people of Europe found them.

I told him about our English Parliament, which makes laws for the country.

"There are two Houses," I said. "Certain great families have a place in the House of Lords. That place is passed down from father to son, so the lords can always give the ruler good advice. They look at every law that the House of Commons wishes to pass, to be sure that it is a good law for the country. And they are the last judges; they say whether the law court judges have been fair or not."

The king had more questions to ask me.

"How are these men trained?" he wanted to know. "The training is long and difficult, I'm sure, for men who have to give advice with no thought of any reward for themselves; men who have to know which law is good for the country (and not for themselves); men who must understand the law better than the judges in the courts. Do they begin this training as boys, or as young men?"

I told him that, until their fathers died and they took their places in the House of Lords, the young men played games, for fun or to win money. They rode horses, trying to catch an animal called a fox. And some of them passed very many hours learning how to fight. The country was very proud of its House of Lords, I told him.

"The other House," I said, "is called the House of Commons. It is made up of gentlemen who have been sent to Parliament by the people to speak for the people. They do this without pay, and often at great cost to themselves, because they wish to serve the people. Any new law first passes through the House of Commons before the House of Lords sees it, and if the ruler and his advisers want more money from the people, they must ask the House of Commons."

I had to answer a great many questions about the House of Commons. The King of Brobdingnag did not understand the readiness of the gentlemen in the House to serve the people without reward, often losing a great deal of money.

"They seem to be wonderful men," he said. "Is there *no* danger that some of them may be rather less good than you think? May not some of them get a place in the House in ways that are not quite so good? Perhaps because they do not mind taking money for passing laws that the ruler and his friends want, or for getting more money from the people for the ruler or his friends?"

I tried to make him understand. There were very many things about my country that he could not understand. Perhaps some of his difficulties were caused by the way I spoke his language. He could not understand our law courts. In Brobdingnag, laws must be very simple, and no law may have more than twenty-two words. So the king was surprised when I told him about the number of men who must speak in a court of law to help the judge to see what a law means, and what is right and what is wrong.

I gave him a very short history of my country.

"I do not like," he said, "to hear about so many wars, and about how much they cost your country. Your people must love to quarrel, or your country must be among very bad countries. Perhaps, my little Grildrig," he said, "your travels have made you wiser and better than the little people you have told me about. You seem quite good – though rather foolish because, of course, your head is so small. But the other things like you in your country seem to be very bad little creatures who ought not to go on living in the world."

I did not want the king to believe that, just because we are small people with small heads, we cannot think and have no science or scientists. So I began to tell him about the powder that our scientists first made about three or four hundred years ago.

"If we gather a lot of this powder together," I said, "and then make the smallest amount of fire touch it, it explodes – it all flies up into the air at once, with a great noise. We can push the powder into a very strong pipe-like thing of iron called a gun. Then we push a ball of iron down the gun and set fire to the powder. The ball flies out and breaks or kills anything it hits. A ball from the biggest gun will kill a great number of soldiers all at once. Or it will break down the strongest wall, or send the biggest ship to the bottom of the sea."

"Who can make this powder?" the king asked me.

"Any man who has been to good schools can make it," I said. "I myself can make the mixture. And I can show your workmen how to make guns as big as your people need. The biggest needn't be more than sixty metres long. With twenty or thirty guns like that, you could break down the walls of the strongest town in your country in a few hours. Or you could bring down every building in this city if its people – for some reason – rose against you."

"Stop!" the king said. "Never speak about such things again. If you say anything about these things to anybody in my country, you will die."

I was surprised at this. And of course my English readers will be surprised. The king was not foolish in other ways. He was a good ruler who understood many things, but he seemed to think that it was wrong to hurt people or to remain a king when the people wanted a change.

"Your kings and lords, and your gentlemen in Parliament," he said, "don't serve the people of your country. Any man who can make two plants – grass, or corn, or other food – grow where only one plant grew before serves his people better than all your rulers and judges and men of law and soldiers and scientists."

Chapter 3
How I came home again

When I had been two years in the country, the king and queen made a journey to the towns and cities in the south. They took Glumdalclitch and me with them, and I travelled in my own box.

We arrived near the sea at last. The journey had made Glumdalclitch and me very tired. I wanted to see the sea again, so I said to Glumdalclitch: "We're both rather unwell, but the sea air will be good for us. Let's go down to the sea."

She called one of the servant boys to carry my box, and we went down to the seaside. The boy put my box on a rock. He had carried my box rather roughly, and I felt ill.

"I must sleep for a time," I told Glumdalclitch.

She helped me to shut my windows and my door so that I should be safe. Then I went to sleep.

Suddenly I woke up. Something had taken hold of the ring in the top of my box, and I felt the box going up and up into the air and then along, very fast.

I moved to one of my windows to see what was happening. I could see nothing through the window – only clouds and the sky.

Then I knew. One of the great seabirds of the country was carrying me away. And I knew what it would do next. Near its home it would drop me on the rocks from high up in the air. My box would break to pieces, and the bird would carry me to its young ones for food.

My box began to move very roughly – up and down and every way. I saw that two other seabirds were fighting the one that was carrying me. It dropped my box, and I was really frightened as it fell faster and faster towards...

There was a great noise, and then darkness, as my box fell into the sea. Then it rose and floated.

I was very glad then that the queen's woodworker had made my box so strong. I was alive, and very little water was coming in. But I did not know what was going to happen to me.

My box floated for several days. I was wondering whether I was going to die of cold, or for want of food and water, or because of great winds, when I heard a noise and felt my box strike something hard.

There was the sound of something moving the ring on the top of my box. Then my box was pulled up about a metre higher than it was before. I thought I heard voices, so I shouted in all the languages I knew.

Something or somebody moved on top of the box, and then I heard, in English:

"Is anybody there?"

"Yes," I shouted. "I'm an Englishman. Please save me."

"You're safe," the voice answered. "Your box is held to the side of our ship, and one of our men is coming to cut a hole in the box to let you out."

"There's no need to waste time doing that," I called. "Just put your finger through the ring in the top of the box and pull the box out of the water. Then take it to the captain's room and put it on his table."

I did not know why they laughed. I had not thought that I could be speaking to men who were no bigger than myself.

The man came and cut a hole in the top of my box and passed down a line for me to climb up.

When I was in the ship and saw the men, I thought at first that they were funny little creatures. I had seen only the huge people of Brobdingnag for two years.

"Why are you shouting?" the captain asked.

I had to tell him all about the country in which I was a small creature who must shout to make the huge people hear him.

After a time, and with many things from the box to show that I was speaking the truth, he believed me. But I knew that my story was not easy to believe.

I myself found it hard to believe that I was back in a world of people no bigger than myself. Even when I was at home with my family I sometimes laughed because everything seemed so small.

Gulliver in the land of the Houyhnhnms

Chapter 1
Houyhnhnms and Yahoos

I stayed in England with my family for several months. But at last my love of travel made me listen to a man who wanted a captain for his ship.

We sailed in September 1710. For a month we went well, but then we were for a long time without any wind. We could not move, and a very bad illness was passed from one to another among the sailors.

There were soon too few sailors to work, and when the wind blew again, I sailed to Barbados to get more men. I did not know that several of the new men were pirates of the worst kind.

The pirates made the other men help them to take the ship and to keep me alone in a small room. Their plan was to turn the ship into a pirate ship and fight against other ships to steal from them.

They sent food and drink to me, but I did not know where we were going. Perhaps they themselves did not know, because a great wind drove the ship far out of our way. In May 1711 they saw land, and they took me to it in the ship's small boat. They left me there and sailed away.

I began to walk away from the sea. There were fields of good grass, trees, and fields of oats. I walked carefully, wondering what the people of this land were like. I was glad the sailors had given me back my sword.

I came to a road, and I saw the footmarks of men without shoes, of cows, and mostly of horses. At last I saw several animals in a field, and a few of the same kind sitting in trees. They were very dirty and very ugly. The males had a lot of hair on their heads, in a line down their backs and down the front of their legs and feet. The males also had beards like goats. The rest of their bodies had no hair. The females had longer hair on their heads but less hair on their bodies, and they were rather smaller than the males.

I had never seen such ugly animals in any of my travels. The sight of them made me feel sick, so I walked on along the road.

I had not gone far when I met one of these ugly creatures coming along the road towards me. He stopped and looked hard at me, making his face even uglier. He reached out his front foot – rather like a hairy hand – to touch me, but I struck him with the side of my sword. I did not want to wound him because I was afraid it might make the people angry if I wounded one of their animals. But he was hurt, and he cried out. His cry brought about forty more of the creatures from the nearest field. They shouted and made angry noises. I moved to a tree and stood with my back to it. I kept them away by waving my sword, but some of them climbed up the tree on the other side and threw dirt down at me.

Suddenly the animals all ran away as fast as they could. I wondered what had made them run away, but I started walking along the road again. Then I saw the cause of their running away.

A horse was walking gently towards me. He was surprised when he saw me, and he looked carefully at my face and hands and feet, walking round me several times.

Another horse came up, and the two horses touched their right front feet together and made sounds to each other several times. They were the sounds that horses make to friends, but I noticed changes in their voices, as if they were speaking some kind of language.

They moved a few metres away and began to walk up and down together, still seeming to talk about me. I was not very happy about the way they were behaving, so I began to walk away. But the first horse, a black one, made a sound that was clearly an order to stop.

The two horses came near to me, looking closely at my face and hands. The black horse rubbed my hat all round with his right front foot, and moved it so much that I had to take the hat off and put it on again. That seemed to surprise both the black horse and his friend, who was brown. The brown horse felt my coat, and found that it was not a part of me like skin. That made them wonder still more.

They began to talk about me again, and I heard that they really were speaking a language. One of the words that they each said several times sounded like *Yahoo*. I tried to say it to myself, making the sounds as horse-like as I could.

When the two horses had stopped speaking for a minute, I said the word to them: *Yahoo*.

They were most surprised, and the black horse said the word twice, clearly trying to teach me to say it better. I did say it better, although not very well. The brown horse gave me a second word to try – a much more difficult one: *Houyhnhnm*. I tried to say it in a horse-like way, not very well at first, but getting better. They both seemed very surprised.

After some more talk, which seemed to be about me, the two friends touched their front right feet again, and the brown horse went away. The black horse made me understand that I must walk in front of him, and I thought it would be wise to go with him. When I walked too slowly, he cried *Hhuun, Hhuun*. I knew his meaning, and I showed him, as well as I could, that I was very tired and could not walk faster. He let me rest.

The horse looks at Gulliver's feet and hands

After a time, we arrived at a house. I thought, "Now I'll see the man who owns the horse and has trained him so well." But the servants were all horses, and when we reached the best rooms, the black horse called out, and a good-looking female horse and two young horses came to look at me. It was clear that the black horse was the owner of the house and these were his wife and children.

The female looked at my hands and face, and I could see that she hated me, as she turned to the black horse and spoke to him. I heard the word *Yahoo* several times. I did not understand it then, although it was the first word I had tried to say.

The black horse led me to a low building at some distance from the house. In it there were three of the hateful creatures that I had first met. They were tied to the wall. The black horse called a young reddish horse, who was one of his servants, and gave him an order.

The reddish horse brought one of the hateful creatures out and made him stand beside me. Then both the owner and the servant looked carefully at the creature and myself, and I heard the word *Yahoo* several times. Then I understood. The beastly creature was just like a man. Its front feet were just like my hands, but hairier and dirtier. Its face was like mine but wider and, again, dirtier.

The Yahoo's feet were like mine, but the horses could not see that, because I had shoes on. The rest of our bodies were the same too, but the horses could not see that because of my clothes. This was what the horses could not understand, because they did not understand my clothes.

The reddish horse tried to give me food of several kinds. The Yahoos were eating meat of some kind, but it had such a bad smell that I could not eat it. Then he showed me the dry grass that the horses ate, and uncooked oats. I could not eat them, and I thought I must die if I did not meet some men – I still could not think of the beastly Yahoos as men.

Then I saw one of the servant horses leading a cow, and I showed that I would like to have some of her milk. A young female servant horse led me to a room where milk was kept, all very clean and healthy. She gave me a large pot of milk, and I drank it very gladly.

Later I taught myself to make a kind of bread with oats. With that, and milk, and some fruit that I found on trees, I lived a very healthy life. I never ate the meat that the hateful Yahoos liked so much.

At night the black horse – I shall call him my owner – ordered the servants to give me a place to sleep in. It was only a few metres from the house, not near the place for the Yahoos.

Chapter 2
How the Houyhnhnms lived

The first thing I wanted to do was to learn the language of my owner and the other horses – the Houyhnhnms.

My owner and his family, and all his servants too, wanted to teach me, because they were surprised that an animal (myself) could behave like a thinking being. My owner wanted so much to learn about me that he himself gave a lot of time to teaching me. He was sure (he told me later) that I must be a Yahoo, but I was clean, I could learn, and I behaved well, and none of these things was true of the Yahoos, who were used for work on the farm but who could not be trained to behave well.

He wanted to know where I came from, and how I was taught to behave like a thinking being, because the Yahoos could not be taught. I told him that I came over the sea from another land in a ship (a great floating thing made of wood) with others like me. The others, I said, made me leave the ship here.

"You have made a mistake," he said. "You have said the thing which is not."

I did not fully understand him then. Later it became clear to me. There is no word in the Houyhnhnms' language for untruths, and yet he could not believe that any beasts could cause a thing of wood to move where they wanted it to go on the water. He was sure no Houyhnhnm could make such a wooden thing, and if he did, he would never let Yahoos go in it.

For the Houyhnhnms, the use of language is to make the speakers understand each other. If anyone *says the thing which is not,* they say, his hearer cannot understand him, so language is useless. My owner never understood me when I spoke about the way men in my country used truth or untruths, and often said what was not true, in order to win something or get power over others.

"If you *say the thing which is not,*" my owner said later, "you are not understood, and so language is useless."

The Houyhnhnms keep Yahoos as farm animals, to pull and carry. There are buildings for them, not too near their owner's house (because of the smell), but when they are not working, they are kept in fields.

The Yahoos seemed to love dirt and everything bad, and the Houyhnhnms could not understand that. All other animals like to be clean, and the Houyhnhnms noticed that I kept myself clean too, and I was not like their Yahoos in that way.

But they also noticed that female Yahoos were excited when I was near them. And when they understood my clothes, they also knew that I was just like a Yahoo, but cleaner, less hairy, and with softer hands and feet.

The Yahoos quarrelled a lot and fought each other for food, for females, for the best places, or for no reason at all. They were lazy, and they behaved very badly whenever they could.

There is no word for *bad* in the Houyhnhnms' language, but they use the word *yahoo* for a servant's foolishness (*hhnm yahoo*), a child's mistake (*whnaholm yahoo*), a stone that cuts their feet, strong winds and heavy rain or hail, and other things that they do not like.

The Houyhnhnms teach their young ones to be clean, hardworking, friendly and kind. They must be strong and healthy. Once every four years the young Houyhnhnms from each part of the country meet for games and running and jumping. The reward for the winner is a song about him or her, made and sung by a friend.

Once every four years there is an Assembly, when the heads of families meet to talk about the country's health and other matters. There was an Assembly after I had been in the country for three years. My owner went to it, and came back rather sad.

Chapter 3
How I came home again

My owner said to me: "I am very sad, but I must tell you what the Assembly advised. They do not like my keeping a Yahoo in my family, as if he were a Houyhnhnm and not an animal. They know that you are better than the other Yahoos, and that you can learn. They are afraid that you will become a leader of the Yahoos and lead them against us. They advised me to send you away. I don't like giving you this order, but you must make one of the floating things that you have spoken about, and you must go. My servants will help you to make the thing."

I understood.

I asked only for the help of the young reddish horse, who seemed to like me. In six weeks we made a boat of the kind the American Indians make: a light wooden form with a covering of skins – mine was covered with the skins of male Yahoos. I had a sail made of skins of the same animal. We put food and milk and water into the boat, and then I was ready to go.

I sailed for very many days towards where I thought India might be. But I saw nothing. I was nearly dead when a ship came in sight.

It was a Portuguese ship, and the Portuguese captain was very kind to me and treated me very well.

I found it very hard at first to believe that these Yahoos could be good. It was surprising to hear them using language (I know the Portuguese language and I could understand them).

The captain did not at first believe my story, and this made me angry because I did not remember the way men used the truth. He seemed to think that I *said the thing which is not*, and that is why I was angry.

But at last he believed me. He was very kind to me and took me to Lisbon. There he helped me to get on a ship for England.

It was a long time before I learnt to live with men and not notice the ways in which they were like Yahoos. Today I am not angry when I meet beasts in the form of men, but I am always angry when they are unkind to horses. I cannot forgive Yahoos who are dirty in mind and body, who do not care for truth, and who are proud. Because the Houyhnhnms were never proud, although they were so good that they had more reason to be proud than we have.

Questions

Questions on each chapter

LILLIPUT

1 How I came to Lilliput

1. What happened to the *Antelope*?
2. Why couldn't Gulliver get up off the grass?
3. What food and drink did the Lilliputians give to Gulliver?
4. What had they made into a house for Gulliver?

2 How I lived in Lilliput

1. What did Gulliver do to the men who shot at him?
2. How could the Lilliputians kill Gulliver?
3. What did the king order six very wise men to do?
4. What must the people do when Gulliver comes into the city?

3 How I made war on Blefusco

1. Who talked to Gulliver about the quarrel inside Lilliput?
2. What were the Big-enders?
3. How did Gulliver save his eyes?
4. Why was the King of Lilliput angry?

4 How I came home again

1. Where did Gulliver first see the boat?
2. What living things did Gulliver take with him?
3. Where did he put the living things?
4. What, at first, did the captain think of Gulliver's story?

BROBDINGNAG

1 How I came to Brobdingnag

1. Why did Gulliver go on shore?
2. What were the "forest trees"?
3. Who became Gulliver's teacher and keeper?

4 How far could a horse go in half an hour?
5 Why did Gulliver get weaker and weaker?

2 How I met the king and queen
1 What was Lorbrulgrud?
2 What did the woodworker make for Gulliver?
3 What training did the men in the House of Lords have?
4 How did they keep laws simple in Brobdingnag?
5 Why did Gulliver speak about gunpowder?

3 How I came home again
1 What journey did the king and queen make?
2 What carried Gulliver's box into the air?
3 Why did the box fall into the sea?
4 What did Gulliver say that made the seamen laugh?
5 Why did Gulliver sometimes laugh when he was at home?

IN THE LAND OF THE HOUYHNHNMS

1 Houyhnhnms and Yahoos
1 Who took Gulliver on shore and left him there?
2 Why did the ugly animals run away?
3 What did the horses find out about Gulliver's coat?
4 What was the difference between Gulliver and a Yahoo?
5 What did Gulliver eat and drink?

2 How the Houyhnhnms lived
1 What did Gulliver want to learn?
2 What did Gulliver mean by "a great floating thing made of wood"?
3 What did the Houyhnhnms mean by "the thing which is not"?
4 What did the Houyhnhnms keep Yahoos for?
5 How often did they have something like our Olympic Games?

3 How I came home again
1 What did Gulliver's owner order him to do?
2 Who helped Gulliver to make a boat?
3 What kind of boat was it?
4 What was the sail made of?
5 What ship took Gulliver to Europe?

Questions on the whole story

These are harder questions. Read the Introduction, and think hard about the questions before you answer them. Some of them ask for your opinion, and there is no fixed answer.

1 After Brobdingnag, Gulliver shouted a lot. Why?

2 After life with the Houyhnhnms, Gulliver was always angry when people were unkind to horses. Why?

3 We are not told what Gulliver noticed after Lilliput. What do you think he noticed in England?

4 Jonathan Swift used satire to make people think about the foolishness of many of the things they did or believed. For example, he showed the foolishness of religious wars or quarrels by describing the quarrel between the Big-enders and the Little-enders in Lilliput. What kind of foolishness do you think Swift was satirising in these examples?
a The titles of the King of Lilliput on page 13.
b The signing of the peace treaty between Lilliput and Blefusco (pages 17–18)
c The Brobdingnag farmer's use of Gulliver to make money (pages 28–30).
d The examination of Gulliver by the learned men of Brobdingnag (pages 31–2).
e The description of England on pages 33–4.
f Gulliver's description of the House of Lords (page 36).
g The talk about guns and gunpowder (pages 38–9).
h The Yahoos' way of behaving (pages 51–2).

5 Why do you think *Gulliver's Travels* (usually in a shortened form) has had so much success as a children's book?

6 Find something good or kind to say about:
a the King of Lilliput
b the King of Blefusco
c the King of Brobdingnag
d Glumdalclitch
e Gulliver'sHouyhnhnm owner.

New words

advice
When we tell other people what we think they ought to do, we are giving them **advice**. We are **advising** them.

assembly
a meeting to talk about such matters as public order

creature
a living person or animal

dish
a big plate for food for more than one person

doll
a plaything in the form of a small person or baby

female
A woman is **female**, a man is **male**. Animals are also female or male. You can say **a female, a male**.

float
stay on top of the water

hail
rain in the form of ice

Houyhnhnm
Say /hw'ɪnem/. It is like the sound a horse makes.

language
words; the way of speaking in a country

oats
corn that horses like

Parliament
the men and women who meet together to make laws for a country

pirate
a sea thief

reward
something that we give to a person who has done well

satire
writing (etc) that makes us see (and laugh at) the foolishness of some of the things we do or believe

string
a thin but strong line of twisted cotton or silk

style
way of using words